Introduction

The Ancient Egyptians were one of the great ancient civilisations that gre~
the river valleys of Africa and Asia over five thousand years ago. There is
evidence in existence today that tells us about how they lived. Some of tl
from the pyramids to papyrus scrolls and in tombs, is testament to the wide use they
made of mathematics in their culture. This book aims to provide a source of
information and ideas for both teachers and children in junior schools about the
mathematics that the Ancient Egyptians used and developed as their civilisation grew.

The book is organised into the following four sections:

▲ About the Ancient Egyptian People
▲ About the Mathematics of the Ancient Egyptians
▲ About the Activity Sheets
▲ Resource and Information Sheets

About the Ancient Egyptian People

This section gives a brief outline of the Ancient Egyptians to provide an introduction
about the people and set the context for the book and the activities that follow. It gives
information and illustration about where the people came from, where they settled and
how they lived. It highlights some of the kinds of problems that the Ancient Egyptian
people faced and how they needed to be solved through the invention and
development of mathematics.

About the Mathematics of the Ancient Egyptians

This section gives a list of the areas of mathematics that were developed by the
Egyptians and includes: their number system, arithmetic and the ways in which they
carried out calculations, their calendar, measurements and weights that were used,
information about pyramids and their construction, and games and puzzles that they
played in their leisure time.

Each aspect of mathematics is clearly explained, with examples and notes for the
teacher. References are made to the Resource and Information Sheets, also in the book,
that develop these ideas further.

About the Activity Sheets

This section is in two parts and contains photocopiable Activity Sheets designed for
children and the notes for the teacher that support the mathematical ideas within them.
These notes are placed alongside each Activity Sheet for handy reference and give a
clear indication of the main mathematical concepts involved. Some of the possible
outcomes of each activity are also given together with suggestions for follow up and
extensions. There is a chart on page 12 listing the Activity Sheets and providing a
summary of the mathematical content covered by each one.

Resource and Information Sheets

In addition to the Activity Sheets there are photocopiable Resource Sheets that provide
information and ideas that can be used freely by the teacher and children to support
further work about the mathematics of the Egyptians. In many cases, these support the
ideas begun on the Activity Sheets but would need some introduction by the teacher.
Page 38 gives an outline of the content of each sheet.

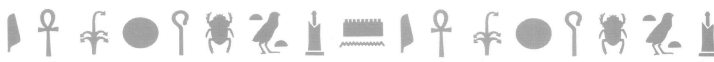

About the Ancient Egyptian People

Who they were, when and where they lived

The civilisation that was Ancient Egypt was one of the oldest in the world. The people of Egypt originated from the heartlands of Africa whose inhabitants were then referred to as Ethiopians. It is thought that they were sent to colonise the fertile lands around the river Nile and their earliest settlements in the Nile valley date from about 4000 BC. The Ethiopian settlers brought many of their ideas with them from Africa, as they sought to preserve their ancient customs and beliefs.

Between 3500 and 3000 BC the separate agricultural communities along the banks of the Nile gradually merged to form two kingdoms. The kingdom that formed around the mouth of the river was called Lower Egypt. Its capital was later called Heliopolis by the Greeks. Further up stream was the Upper Kingdom of Egypt. A legendary figure called Menes, who came from Nubia, which is in present day Sudan, united the whole of Egypt in about 3100 BC and from him began a line of powerful Pharaohs who ruled over the whole empire for the next three thousand years.

At the height of its power during the fifteenth century BC, the Ancient Egyptian empire extended from the banks of the Red Sea to the eastern Mediterranean sea, covering an area that today is the whole of Egypt, part of Libya and Sudan, all of Israel and Lebanon and parts of Syria and Turkey. The capital city, one of the most famous of Ancient Egyptian cities, was Thebes, which was about five hundred miles from the mouth of the River Nile.

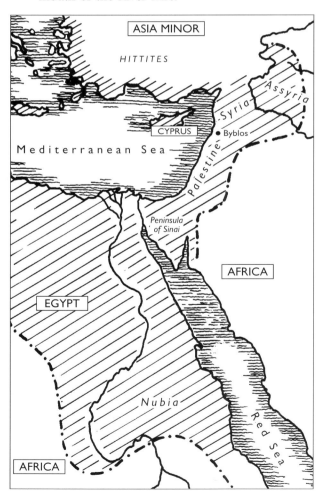

A map of Ancient Egypt

Before Christ (BC)	Time Line
c. 4000	Beginning of the Egyptian civilisation
c. 2920	Union of Upper and Lower Egypt
c. 2620	Step Pyramid built
c. 2530	Great Pyramid built
1333–1323	Rule of Tutankhamun
1290–1224	Rule of Rameses
1285	Battle of Qadesh
700	Rome founded
332	Alexander the Great conquers Egypt
323	Alexander dies
304–284	Rule of Ptolemy
51–30	Rule of Cleopatra
30	Start of Roman rule
After Christ (AD)	
395	Romans leave Egypt
1600	European historians begin to take an interest in the study of Ancient Egypt
1922	Carter discovers the tomb of Tutankhamun

The River Nile is over four thousand miles from its source in the mountains of Abyssinia to its mouth in the Mediterranean Sea. It comes down from the mountains and forests, pours down cataracts and past deep gorges and finally flows down to the shallower parts where the river valley spreads out, before emptying into the sea. Every summer, rain falling on the mountains causes the river to swell. In ancient times, before the building of the Aswan Dam, as the river reached the flat valley, it flooded the land depositing layers of rich black earth on the soil. The Egyptians called this great overflowing of the Nile the 'inundation'. This made the land very fertile and a good place to settle.

The lands surrounding the fertile Nile valley are, however, dry sandy desert. It is these very conditions, that are excellent for preserving things that would otherwise rot in a wetter climate. Religion permeated all aspects of the life of the ancient Egyptians and it found expression in a wide variety of forms. The Egyptians built great tombs, magnificent temples and monuments that housed many artefacts, valuables and written texts. Walls and statues were decorated with pictures and inscriptions that revealed much about their customs, beliefs and way of life. It is these two aspects, climate and religion, that have enabled so much to be preserved about the Ancient Egyptians and ensure that we know so much about this great ancient civilisation today.

How the Egyptians lived, what their society was like

The Egyptians were farmers and farming the fertile land made them rich. With this wealth came power. They conquered many other lands and the conquered people were made to pay 'tribute' which further increased their wealth. Trade flourished, and many beautiful and valuable things like gold, spices and rare woods were brought back from other lands. With their wealth, the Egyptians were able to build great cities and temples, monuments and tombs.

They worshipped many gods. One of their most important gods was Ra, the Sun-God. The Egyptians believed that their kings were also Gods and would live on after death in their tombs and so they buried things that they would need in the after-life. These

were often valuable and so passage-ways into tombs were secret. Despite this, many tombs were plundered. The tomb of Tutankhamun, discovered in 1922, was found to be whole and untouched; and from evidence found there archeologists have found out much about the Ancient Egyptian way of life.

The Egyptians discovered a way of making paper using papyrus leaves, and devised a system of writing words and numbers. Men who learnt to write were called scribes and they were important and honoured people. Artefacts and pictures on the walls of tombs and pyramids, together with books and scrolls recorded the life and work of the Egyptian people.

Stone carving showing hieroglyphic text (British Museum)

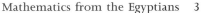

The sorts of problems the Egyptians needed to solve

We can surmise that one of the features that transformed Egypt from a marshy area containing scattered settlements into one of the great ancient civilisations, was the gradual development of effective methods of flood control, irrigation and marsh drainage. This would have contributed to a significant increase in agricultural yield, making the community much richer. However each of these innovations required great knowledge and organisation. An irrigation system calls for digging canals and constructing reservoirs and dams. Marsh drainage and flood control require substantial co-operation between what were scattered settlements. The Egyptian farmers also needed to be able to prepare for and predict when the annual flood would occur.

> The Ancient Egyptians needed a way of keeping records of dates and measurements of the water levels of the river. They kept astrological records and from these constructed some of the earliest calendars. They also devised ways of measuring and recording the depth of water in the river using linear measuring rods.

Scarce arable land needed to be parcelled out fairly amongst the growing population and frequent land measurements would need to be taken after each flood to ensure that this was maintained by the rightful owner. Herodotus, the Greek historian who lived in the fifth century BC, tells of the obliteration of land boundaries by the encroaching Nile and how the regular services of surveyors, known as 'harpedonaptai' (literally meaning 'rope stretchers'), were needed.

'Sesos [Pharaoh Rameses II, c. 1300 BC] divided the land into lots and gave a square piece of equal size to everybody; from the produce he exacted an annual tax'.

> The Egyptians developed accurate ways of measuring land area, boundaries and angles as well as special ways of dividing amounts, using fractions.

The territory of the Ancient Egyptian civilisation at the height of its power was vast. Control by the centralised government of the Pharaohs over such a large expanse of land required an efficient administration system. Censuses had to be taken, records needed to be kept, taxes calculated, recorded and collected, produce stored, and large armies maintained.

> In order to record and process this information, the Egyptians developed an efficient number system, numerical script and ways of calculating solutions to numerical problems.

As the Egyptian civilisation matured there evolved financial, trading and commercial practices with peoples from other lands as well within their own civilisation. They needed to agree how they were to measure crops, such as corn and other agricultural produce, and spices and valuable metals which they imported from elsewhere.

> This necessitated the creation of a standard system of weights and measures so that fair exchanges could be made.

The construction of cities, temples and tombs required many geometric skills and practices to be developed, technological tools devised and accurate measurements taken. The high point of this practical mathematical culture was the construction of the pyramids.

> The Ancient Egyptians devised ways of constructing level squares, cutting accurate cuboid blocks, orientating buildings to face east, west, north and south and calculating measurements of triangulation.

With the development of efficient working practices and in a culture where the wealthy and titled had slaves and servants, there would be increased leisure time.

The Egyptians developed recreational activities which included logical and strategic mathematical games.

Much evidence of Egyptian mathematics is recorded on papyrus which was the writing medium of the time. There are two major sources: the Ahmes Papyrus, named after the scribe who composed it in about 1650 BC from a work three centuries earlier (also named the Rhind Mathematical Papyrus after the British collector who acquired it in 1858), and the Moscow Papyrus written in about 1850 BC and brought to Russia in the middle of the last century. These both contain mathematical problems together with their solutions.

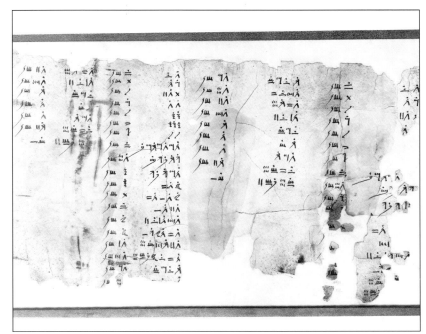

Extract from the Mathematical Leather Roll containing simple relations between fractions (British Museum)

About the mathematics of the Ancient Egyptians

The areas of mathematics that the Egyptians used and developed included:

▲ The Egyptian number system
▲ Egyptian arithmetic and fractions calculations
▲ The Egyptian calendar
▲ Measurements of land area and boundaries
▲ Egyptian standardised weights
▲ Construction of pyramids and temples
▲ Egyptian games and puzzles

Egyptian number system

The oldest known numeral systems were those developed by the ancient Egyptians and those being developed during the same period of time by the Sumerians in Southern Babylon. Over the years, the Egyptians evolved three distinct systems of notation with which they recorded their numbers.

The earliest system was called the hieroglyphic system and it made use of a pictorial script to represent individual numbers. Clear imprints could be made on stone or metal using this form of notation.

The Egyptians then developed a more economical system of writing which was called the hieratic system. Their development was made possible by the greater freedom allowed by the use of pen and ink on papyrus. The hieratic system began to be developed during the Old Kingdom and important mathematical texts such as the Ahmes Papyrus 1650 BC, and the Moscow Papyrus written in 1850 BC both use hieratic symbols.

Extract from the Rhind Papyrus (British Museum)

Later, during the Greek and the Roman periods of Egyptian history 330 BC, they used a popular system of notation which was a further adaptation of the hieratic system which was called demotic.

What was important, mathematically, was that each of these systems used base ten.

Details about the first two types of script are given below and the Resource Sheet: Egyptian Numerals, gives further examples of these three types of script and can be used as a reference with children.

Hieroglyphic numerals

The hieroglyphic system could be described as a tallying system in that groups of repeated symbols were made to denote larger numbers. It was a primitive form of numeration requiring a large number of symbols to represent numbers. Hieroglyphs were written from right to left but because there were different symbols representing one, ten, hundred, etc., there would be no confusion if they were written in a different order, unlike our own system of numerals.

In the hieroglyphic pictorial script, each character represented an object. Special symbols, based on a rope, were used to represent each power of ten from 1 to 10^7. A unit was represented as a short piece of rope, ten was a longer piece shaped like a horseshoe and a hundred was a coil of rope. The symbol for a thousand looked like a lotus flower but also formed the initial of the word 'khaa', meaning 'measuring cord'. Ten thousand was represented by a kind of crooked finger, a hundred thousand, as a stylised tadpole and a million was represented by a man with arms upraised as if in astonishment at the vastness of the number. Ten million was represented by a sun which could have been associated with one of the most powerful of Egyptian deities – Ra, the Sun-God.

1	10	10^2	10^3	10^4	10^5	10^6

Any number could be written using the symbols additively. For example:

$$2321 \quad = \quad 2(10^3) \quad + \quad 3(10^2) \quad + \quad 2(10) \quad + \quad 1$$

Hieratic numerals

The hieratic system was similar to the hieroglyphic system in that it was additive and used base ten. It was, however, much more symbolic and numerals were often abbreviations of hieroglyphic symbols. The development of the hieratic system was an important step forward in the development of numeration as numbers required fewer symbols. Symbols, although being much simpler to write were, however, more difficult to remember. For example:

1	2	3	4	5	6	7	8	9	10	20	30	100	1000

An example of the economy of the hieratic system over the use of hieroglyphic symbols can be illustrated if we consider the number nine hundred and ninety-nine.

Hieroglyphic   Hieratic   Modern

27 symbols   10 symbols   3 symbols

Egyptian arithmetic

Addition and subtraction

Addition and subtraction presented no difficulty in a system that was additive in its structure, one merely added or took away the number of symbols, making a collection of like symbols or replacing a hieroglyph of larger value with ten smaller ones. The

Egyptians used an interesting symbol to represent addition. This looked like a pair of legs walking forwards. For subtraction this was reversed, with the legs walking backwards. To show equivalence or 'equals', the Egyptians used a symbol that looked like some scales. An example is given below. Egyptians did not need to know any addition tables. It is thought that the Egyptians used an abacus when carrying out addition and subtraction calculations before recording their results.

Multiplication

Multiplication by powers of ten was a simple process and involved substituting symbols with those representing numbers that were ten times bigger. For example:

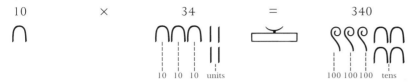

Although the Egyptians did use this method of multiplication they mainly used a different principle. From the Ahmes papyrus, we know that this involved the process of repeatedly doubling numbers and adding numbers and formed the basis of their system of multiplication and division.

For example, to multiply 15 by 13 the Egyptians would first double 15 and then double again. This would give:

$2 \times 15 = 30$ (double 30) $4 \times 15 = 60$

Doubling again would give:

(double 60) $8 \times 15 = 120$

and by adding 15, 60 and 120 (1, 4 and 8 times 15), they would obtain $13 \times 15 = 195$.

This was often written in tabulated form:

13	×	15
1		15
~~2~~		~~30~~
4		60
8		120
		195 = 13 × 15

Since 13×15 was required and $(1 + 4 + 8) = 13$, the Egyptians crossed off 2×13 and added what they needed $(15 + 60 + 120) = 195 = (13 \times 15)$.

This ancient method of multiplication provided the foundation for all Egyptian calculation and was widely used, with some modification, by the Greeks. It continued to be used even in the Middle Ages in Europe when modern numerals were coming into use. Modern variations of this method are still popular among rural communities in what was Russia, Ethiopia and the Near East.

Division

The Egyptians carried out the process of division using a method closely related to their method of multiplication. In the Ahmes Papyrus, division is introduced by the words, 'reckon with a number so as to obtain another number'. Rather than thinking of dividing 121 by 11 an Egyptian scribe would say: 'reckon with 11 so as to get 121', in other words, 'starting with 11, how many times would I need to add 11 to itself to get 121?'

The calculation would be written as,

1	11
2	22
+̶	+̶+̶
8	88

Look at the 11 times table above, you will see that $11 + 22 + 88 = 121$, which is obtained by adding together $1 + 2 + 8$ giving 11; since 11 elevens would be needed to give 121, then 121 divided by 11 is 11.

Calculations that could not be done in this way were those that required fractions. The Egyptians were constrained by the fact that their system of numeration did not allow for a way of expressing fractions. They invented an ingenious way of resolving this problem.

Fractions

The Egyptians had special words and symbols for the fractions that served everyday purposes, like $\frac{1}{2}$, $\frac{1}{3}$, $\frac{2}{3}$, $\frac{1}{4}$, and $\frac{3}{4}$. They also developed a standard notation for unit fractions. To denote the unit fraction, $\frac{1}{12}$ for instance, they wrote the denominator, 12, under the hieroglyph for 'part'. For example:

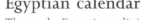

Much of our knowledge of Egyptian mathematics has been derived from the Ahmes Papyrus but another important source of information was the Mathematical Leather Roll. It looked very much like a pupil's notebook and was found near the Ahmes Papyrus. The Leather Roll contained relationships between unit fractions and helped mathematicians to make sense of the problems and solutions contained in the Ahmes Papyrus, rather like our own multiplication tables, would help in multiplication calculations.

For example:

$$\frac{1}{6} + \frac{1}{6} = \frac{1}{3} \quad \text{and} \quad \frac{1}{2} + \frac{1}{3} + \frac{1}{6} = 1$$

$$\frac{1}{3} + \frac{1}{6} = \frac{1}{2} \quad \text{and} \quad \frac{1}{5} + \frac{1}{20} = \frac{1}{4}$$

Egyptian calendar

The early Egyptians divided the year into 12 months of 30 days each, with five days added on at the end of the year. Their interest in the stars was illustrated by pictures in the tombs showing astronomical features, including maps of star positions, to calculate the passage of night hours. They devised a system of daylight and night time hours, which formed the origin of our own system of the division of the day into 24 hours. Because of the different lengths of days and nights during the different seasons, hours of different lengths were used at different times of the year.

The Egyptians were the first to use a sundial in the fifteenth century BC. It was in the form of a shadow stick and had a straight base with a raised gnomon at one end. This was set to face east in the morning and west in the afternoon and the base had six divisions for hours. Egyptians may also have used large obelisks, usually dedicated to the sun-god, as sundials.

Sand-timers were the earliest form of time keeper and these were certainly used by the Egyptians but could only be used for measures of limited duration. Egyptians developed water-clocks which consisted of a stone bowl with a small opening at the bottom. Seasonal adjustments were made by reading levels of lines on the sides of the bowl.

Egyptian water-clock (British Museum)

Land measurements

Egyptian linear measurements were based on the length of the forearm and called the 'royal cubit'. This was broken down into smaller units called the 'palm' and the 'digit'. The palm was the width of the palm, excluding the thumb and the digit was a finger's-breadth.

Relationships between the measures were as follows:

$$4 \text{ digits} = 1 \text{ palm}$$
$$7 \text{ palms} = 1 \text{ cubit}$$

There are Egyptian representations of surveyors using knotted rope, where the knots represent divisions of linear measurement, and measuring rods.

Measures or area were based on the cubit with a rectangle one cubit by 100 cubits also being called a cubit. 100 of these rectangles were called a square 'khet'.

Further information about the measures that the ancient Egyptians used and their equivalent measurements today can be found in the Resource Sheet: Weights and Measures.

The Ahmes Papyrus reveals that the Egyptians used geometrical calculations based on the right-angled triangle and understood many of its properties. They showed knowledge of the integral numbers of units in the length (3, 4, 5, 5, 12, 13).

Egyptian capacity and weights

Eye of Horus

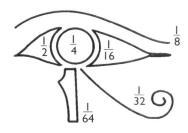

Relationships between measures of capacity were as follows:
32 'ro' = 1 'hin'
10 'hennu' (plural of 'hin') = 1 'hekat'
20 or 16 'hekat' = 1 'khar', meaning 'sack'.

Egyptians, from the time of the eighteenth dynasty, used the 'kite' and 'deben' as their measures for the weights of metals. 10 'kite' were equivalent to 1 'deben'. As they had no form of developed coinage, payments in general were often assessed in terms of weighted amounts of metal.

Further information can be found in the Resource Sheet: Weights and Measures.

The 'hekat' was the official Egyptian measure for corn and smaller measures were in the fractions $\frac{1}{2}$, $\frac{1}{4}$, $\frac{1}{8}$, $\frac{1}{16}$, $\frac{1}{32}$ and $\frac{1}{64}$ of a 'hekat'. These were written in a pictogram of symbols known as Horus Eye, shown left. There was a legend that the god, Horus, had an eye torn apart in a fight, and these parts were later restored by the god, Thoth.

An Egyptian weighing gold rings against a weight in the form of a bull's head. New Kingdom, c. 1400 BC (British Museum)

Construction of pyramids and temples

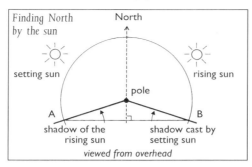

Finding North by the sun

North

setting sun

rising sun

pole

A

B

shadow of the rising sun

shadow cast by setting sun

viewed from overhead

The Egyptians used their knowledge of geometry in the construction of the pyramids. Care was taken to achieve a north-south-east-west orientation for the pyramids. North-south orientation could easily be established by finding the direction of a shadow cast by the noonday sun. A vertical pole was set up in the sand and the path traversed by the tip of its shadow could be observed. The points A and B, where this intersected a suitable circle drawn around the pole, would be joined. Then the line AB was bisected at right angles to establish the direction of the sun at midday. An alternative would be to bisect the angle formed by the rising and setting positions of a star.

Most Egyptian pyramids were square-based with the apex directly above the centre point of the square base. The gradient of the pyramid, known as its 'batter', was in the form of a ratio. It was expressed in terms of the number of palms in half the length of a side of the base, per cubit of vertical height (1 cubit = 7 palms).

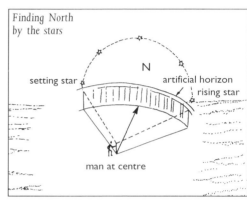

Finding North by the stars

N

setting star

artificial horizon

rising star

man at centre

For example:

a pyramid 98 cubits in vertical height

with a side length of 140 cubits (or 7 × 140 in palms)

would have a 'batter' of $\dfrac{\text{half the length of the side}}{\text{vertical height}}$

expressed in palms $= 7 \times \dfrac{70}{98} = 7 \times \dfrac{10}{14} = 7 \times \dfrac{1}{2} = 5$ palms

The dimensions of the Great Pyramid were very carefully fixed and information about this is given in the Resource Sheet: Great Pyramid.

The largest of all the Ancient Egyptian temples was the Temple of Karnak. Although it has lost its roof, the great pillars still stand. Some of them are so enormous that 100 men could stand on the top of each one. It was begun by the Pharaohs during the Middle Kingdom, in about 2000 BC, and added to by nearly all the succeeding rulers. When it was finished, it was so large that you could put the whole of the area of St Paul's Cathedral and the Cathedral of Notre-Dame inside it.

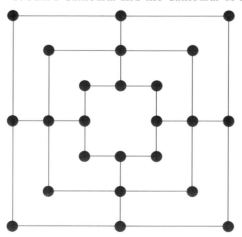

Board for Nine Men's Morris

Egyptian games and puzzles

The invention and playing of games for recreational and intellectual stimulation appears to be a universal human activity and there is evidence that the ancient Egyptians indulged in these activities. The board for an early form of noughts and crosses has been found cut into the roofing slabs of the Egyptian temple at Kurna (c. 1400 BC). This was called Three Men's Morris and involved placing pieces

on a board with the object of getting three in a row. Boards for Nine Men's Morris have also been found in Egypt dating from the same time.

Egyptians today play a modern version of a traditional game called Seega. Again, this involves positioning pieces to obtain a line of either three, or in the traditional game, five in a row. This game has a long history.

Another of the game boards cut into the roofing slabs of the temple at Kurna (c. 1700 BC), is in the form of a pentagram, and a solitaire game called pentalpha is still played on a board like this in Crete today. Two other game boards have been found cut into stone slabs in a small chapel at Deir-el-Medina, near Luxor.

Mancala is a the name given to a family of games in which shells, stones or seeds are 'sown' in holes arranged in two, three or four rows. The word 'Mancala' is taken from 'Mankalha', a version played in Egypt using holes dug in the sand and pebbles or pellets of camel dung. Examples of these types of game can be found all over areas of Africa and Asia today. Descriptions of these Games, together with a copy of the boards used, can be found in Resource Sheets: The Game of Seega, Nine Men's Morris and Mancala.

The earliest known Mancala board (c. 1580–1150 BC), with two rows of holes, was found in Egypt. There are several well-cut sets of holes in the temple of Kurna and others at the temples of Karnak and Luxor. The best set at Kurna has 16 holes about 6 cm wide and 2 cm deep and is approximately 60 cm long.

Race games appear to have been some of the earliest types of game invented and a wall painting of about 2650 BC shows Queen Nefertiti playing either Senat or Tau, a form of backgammon. Tau ('robbers') was discovered

Queen Nefertiti playing either 'Senat' or 'Tau'.

with casting sticks, made of black ebony on one side and white ivory on the other. Also found were 20 carved pieces, ten lions and ten jackals.

The rules of the game are unknown but it is supposed that the coloured squares represented some form of safety area for the pieces and that the ten pieces were required to travel the board in a race.

Found in a tomb at Sakkara (c. 2700 BC) is an illustration of a spiral race game. It shows an equipment box containing six sets of marbles with three lion and three hound figures. The board is in the form of a coiled snake with the head in the centre and the body divided up into a number of spaces, varying from 29 to over 500. Although no rules have been found, it is thought that each player had to guess the number of marbles held in the hand of their opponent. If they were right, they could move that number of spaces; if they were wrong, their opponent could move.

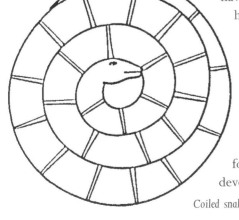

The Ahmes Papyrus, as well as containing mathematical problems of a practical nature, also included some puzzles designed for mathematical stimulation and the development of skills.

Coiled snake race game

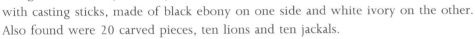

About the Activity Sheets

Each Activity Sheet is designed to stand alone but some are prepared in pairs with the second one developing and extending ideas contained in the first. It may be helpful, if using them in a differentiated way, to invite children to refer to the first in the pair for any information. The sheets are best introduced through discussion with the children to establish the key ideas within them. Teacher support notes provide information on: the task, the mathematics that is involved; some of the possible outcomes of the extension ideas together with suggestions for follow-up.

Number	Title	Outline of content
1	**Egyptian Hieroglyphic Numerals 1**	Place value. Using symbols in multiples, or powers of ten.
2	**Egyptian Hieroglyphic Numerals 2**	Number patterns using number bond. Making and testing predictions.
3	**Egyptian Addition 1**	Place value. Addition using symbols in multiples of ten.
4	**Egyptian Addition 2**	Number bonds in multiples of ten. Number patterns, prediction.
5	**Egyptian Subtraction 1**	Subtraction using symbols in multiples of ten. Number patterns.
6	**Egyptian Subtraction 2**	Subtraction using exchanges of symbols in multiples of ten.
7	**Pyramid numbers 1**	Addition. Number relationships using logical and systematic working.
8	**Pyramid numbers 2**	Addition. Relationships between odd and even numbers, prediction.
9	**Pyramid numbers 3**	Logic. Using addition and subtraction bonds to solve numerical problems.
10	**Egyptian Multiplication 1**	Doubling. Relationship between multiples of 2, 4, 8, 16, and 32.
11	**Egyptian Multiplication 2**	Addition and relationship between + and × using multiples of 2, 4, 8, 16.
12	**Pyramid Builders**	Multiplication and division by 12. Using multiples of 10. Multiples of 30.
13	**Making Pyramids 1**	Using 2D net to construct a pyramid. Predicting, estimating measurement.
14	**Making Pyramids 2**	Multiplication square numbers. Addition. Predicting number sequence.
15	**Pharaohs**	Calculating differences. Ordering dates. Place value to 1000.

Activity Sheets 1 and 2   Egyptian Hieroglyphic Numerals

Task

In Activity Sheet 1, children will be deciphering Egyptian Hieroglyphic numerals and writing the number that is represented. They will also be writing numbers themselves using Hieroglyphic symbols. The challenge is to set some questions for a partner to decipher.

Activity Sheet 2 invites children to count the number of numerals the Egyptians needed in order to write numbers. They are challenged to find a way of predicting the number of numerals needed to write any number.

Mathematics

In Activity Sheet 1, children will be using and applying their knowledge of place value and decoding and encoding using different symbols to represent powers of ten.

In Activity Sheet 2, they will be distinguishing between numerals and numbers and searching for number patterns in their results. They are also involved in predicting events, communicating their findings and proving them.

Possible outcomes

What is interesting about the number of Egyptian Hieroglyphics needed to write numbers is that they form a pattern that can be predicted.

| 12 | uses | 3 Egyptian numerals | and $1 + 2 = 3$ |
| 25 | uses | 7 Egyptian numerals | and $2 + 5 = 7$ |

So if you add together the digits we would use to write the number, then this will tell you how many numerals the Egyptian needed to use. This sum is called the Digital Root of a number.

Follow-up ideas and questions

The Resource Sheet: Egyptian Numerals contains additional information about the Hieroglyphic symbols used to write numbers up to a million. It also gives a chart showing the Hieratic and Demotic scripts developed by the Egyptians. Children could be encouraged to make comparisons between the different types of script used and with the numerals used in our own number system.

e.g.

Q. Which script do you think is the easiest to learn and use? Why?

Q. Which script is the most economical and efficient? Why?

Children can be challenged to predict what sorts of numbers use the most Egyptian Hieroglyphic numerals. It is not necessarily the number with the highest value.

e.g.

Q. What three-digit number would use the most Egyptian numerals?

Q. What three-digit number would use the least?

Q. What is the largest number that could be written using 10 Egyptian numerals?

Q. How many different numbers could be written using 10 Egyptian numerals?

Digital Roots are very interesting to explore in their own right. There are many patterns to be found if you look at the digital roots of the numbers in different multiplication tables.

e.g.

Q. What happens if you add together the digits of multiples of three?

Q. Can you always know if a number is a multiple of three, without doing the division?

Q. What about the digital roots of numbers in the six and nine times table?

The mathematics of the Vedics involved looking at the patterns of digital roots in a tables square.

Egyptian Hieroglyphic Numerals 1

Archeologists have found signs that stood for numbers, that the Egyptians made on stone. They used numerals that were very different from ours. Egyptians used Hieroglyphic numerals.

	stood for	1
∩	stood for	10
?	stood for	100
?	stood for	1000

Example:

∩∩||| is __23__

??? ∩|||| ||| is __517__

What are these numbers?

1 ∩∩∩∩∩|||| is _____

2 ???∩∩∩|| is _____

3 ?? ∩∩∩|||| ∩∩∩|||| is _____

4 ? ? ∩| is _____

5 ? ???∩∩||| ∩∩||| is _____

6 ?? ||||| ||||| is _____

7 ? ? ? ∩∩∩ ∩∩   is _____

8 ? ∩∩∩||| ∩∩∩|| is _____

Write these numbers using Egyptian Hieroglyphic numerals:

9 53

10 28

11 207

12 164

13 320

14 2002

15 4152

16 1049

CHALLENGE

Set some questions for a partner to do.

Try some that only use ten Egyptian Hieroglyphic numerals.

How many different numbers can you make using only ten numerals?

What about 11 numerals?

Egyptian Hieroglyphic Numerals 2

Archeologists have found signs that stood for numbers, that the Egyptians made on stone. Egyptians used Hieroglyphic numerals. They needed to use many numerals to write certain numbers.

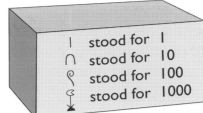

	stood for	1
∩	stood for	10
℗	stood for	100
⚘	stood for	1000

Example:

To write the number 67 the Egyptians used 13 Hieroglyphic numerals ∩∩∩∩∩∩ |||||||

Questions:

Write these numbers using Hieroglyphic numerals. How many Hieroglyphic numerals have been used to write these numbers?

1 12   uses _____ numerals   **2** 9   uses _____ numerals

3 75   uses _____ numerals   **4** 104   uses _____ numerals

5 41   uses _____ numerals

Questions:

How many numerals would the Egyptians have needed to use to write these numbers? (You may want to check this by writing the number in Hieroglyphics on the other side of this paper.)

6 51   used _____ numerals   **7** 64   used _____ numerals

8 88   used _____ numerals   **9** 204   used _____ numerals

10 311   used _____ numerals   **11** 189   used _____ numerals

CHALLENGE

Which numbers use the most number of hieroglyphic numerals to write? Find a way of predicting or working out the number of numerals needed to write any number. Explain or prove your method.

WANT TO FIND OUT MORE?   Look at the Egyptian Numerals Resource Sheet.

Activity Sheets 3 and 4   Egyptian Addition

Task

In Activity Sheet 3 children will be performing additions where they need to repeat the use of the same numeral a number of times and then where they need to exchange ten numerals for one of a value ten times greater. They are challenged to set some questions to give to a partner.

Activity Sheet 4 involves children in counting the number of Egyptian numerals used in certain addition number bonds and to predict and explain the patterns that will result. They are challenged to generalise for other multiples of ten.

Mathematics

In Activity Sheet 3 children will be using and applying their knowledge of place value and the decimal number system and encoding and coding using symbols that represent powers, or multiples of ten.

In Activity Sheet 4 they will be distinguishing between numerals and numbers, using number bonds of 20, 30, 40, 50, and 60 and searching for number patterns in their results. They are also involved in predicting events, communicating their findings and proving them.

Possible outcomes

Looking at the digital roots of number bonds yields a rich source of patterns that can be predicted and generalised.

Egyptian numerals used in bond to 20:

1 + 19   uses 11 numerals   2 + 18   uses 11 numerals
3 + 17   uses 11 numerals   4 + 16   uses 11 numerals

They are always 11 with a few exceptions

10 + 10 uses 2 numerals   0 + 20   uses 2 numerals

Drawing up a table of results for addition number bonds for multiples of ten is really interesting.

Multiple of ten	Egyptian numerals used		
10	10	or	1
20	11	or	2
30	12	or	3
40	13	or	4

Follow up ideas and questions

Children could be encouraged to find a way of expressing the relationship between the multiple of ten and the number of Egyptian numerals used in the addition bonds.

e.g.

Q. If the multiple is 90, what would be the number of numerals used?

Q. What about 240?

This could lead to the formulation of an algebraic expression to describe the relationship. e.g.

In words:

The number of tens minus one then added to ten will give the maximum number of digits used.

In symbols:

$$(n - 1) + 10 = max$$

where n represents the number of tens.

Number bonds other than multiples of ten could be explored.

e.g.

Q. How many Egyptian numerals are used in addition bonds of 25? 106?

Q. Does it make a difference if you have more than two numbers being added?

Egyptian Addition 1

Addition was often quite simple using Egyptian Hieroglyphic numerals because the Egyptians used the same numeral repeatedly. The Egyptians also used special symbols for addition (⋀) and equals (⟅⟆). **For example:**

∩∩|||	⋀	∩∩||	⟅⟆	∩∩∩∩|||||
(23)	added to	(22)	equals	(45)

Do these additions using Egyptian Hieroglyphic numerals:

1 ∩∩∩\| ⋀ ∩∩\|\|\|\| ⟅⟆ _____

2 ⟨\|\|\|\|/\|\|\| ⋀ ∩∩∩∩∩\|\| ⟅⟆ _____

3 ⟨∩∩\|\|\| ⋀ ⟨∩∩\|\|\| ⟅⟆ _____

Sometimes they ended up with more than ten numerals the same.
For example:

∩∩∩\|\| ∩∩∩ (62)   ⋀   ∩∩∩\| ∩∩∩ (51)   ⟅⟆   ┌─────────────┐ ∩∩∩∩∩ \|\|\| ∩∩∩∩∩ (10 tens) and 13   ⟨∩ \|\|\| (exchanged for 1 hundred) and 13

They had to exchange these for the numeral that was the number ten times bigger.

Do these additions that need you to exchange for a numeral that is worth ten times more.

4 ∩∩∩\|\|\| ∩∩∩ ⋀ ∩∩∩\|\|\| ∩∩∩ ⟅⟆ _____ exchange for

5 ∩∩\|\|\|\|/\|\|\| ⋀ ∩\|\|\|\|/\| ⟅⟆ _____ exchange for

6 ⟨∩∩∩ ∩∩∩\| ⋀ ∩∩∩∩∩\|\|\| ∩∩∩\|\| ⟅⟆ _____ exchange for

7 ⟨⟨⟨⟨⟨∩ ⋀ ⟨⟨⟨⟨⟨∩∩ ∩∩ ⟅⟆ _____ exchange for

8 ⟨⟨⟨∩∩ ⟨⟨⟨ ⋀ ⟨∩∩ ⟨⟨⟨ ⟅⟆ _____ exchange for

CHALLENGE Set some Egyptian additions for your partner to do.

Egyptian Addition 2

Some additions form a pattern, especially if you count the number of Hieroglyphic numerals that the Egyptians needed to use.

All these pairs of numbers add up to 30. Write them using Egyptian numerals and count the number of Hieroglyphic numerals used.

1 13 + 17 _____ ∩ _____ Hieroglyphic numerals used _____

2 15 + 15 _____ ∩ _____ Hieroglyphic numerals used _____

3 28 + 2 _____ ∩ _____ Hieroglyphic numerals used _____

4 3 + 27 _____ ∩ _____ Hieroglyphic numerals used _____

5 What do you notice ?

6 Try some other pairs of numbers that total 30 using Egyptian numerals and count the number of Hieroglyphics used.

BRAINTEASER

**Pharaoh Khufu thought of building the great pyramid.
He may have been clever enough to set this brain teaser.**

∩ |||||| ∩   ∩∩ |||| ⌐   ∩∩∩∩
(16)   (24)   (40)

Q. How many numerals are used for the two numbers added? _____

and ∩∩ ||||| ∩   ∩ ||||| ⌐   ∩∩∩∩
(25)   (15)   (40)

Q. How many numerals are used for the two numbers added? _____

**He predicts that for all the pairs of numbers that total 40, the Egyptians would need to use 13 numerals.
Try some pairs of numbers to check if this is right. Explain why this happens.**

CHALLENGE

**Using Egyptian Hieroglyphic numerals, write down some pairs of numbers that total 50. Try to predict the total number of numerals that you need to use for each pair.
What about if the total was 60?....70?**

Activity Sheets 5 and 6 Egyptian Subtraction

Task

In Activity Sheet 5, children will be subtracting one number of numerals from another and recognising that numerals of the same power of ten can be easily subtracted. The challenge invites them to count the number of numerals used in each subtraction and to identify a relationship between them before setting some subtractions for a partner to do.

Activity Sheet 6 involves children in exchanging numerals, for ten others of a ten-times smaller value in order to carry out subtractions. The challenge invites them to set some questions for a partner to do.

Mathematics

In Activity Sheet 5, children will be using and applying their knowledge of subtraction by recognising that only numerals of the same value can be subtracted from one another. The challenge involves them in recognising simple number patterns linked to number bonds and subtraction.

In Activity Sheet 6, children will be using their knowledge of a base-ten number system to exchange numerals of a higher power of ten, for ten others that are equivalent in value.

Possible outcomes

The number of Egyptian numerals needed to write some subtraction question forms an interesting and easily predictable pattern linked to digital roots.

For example:

$$14 \quad - \quad 3 \quad = \quad 11$$

uses this number of Egyptian numerals,

$$5 \qquad 3 \qquad \quad 2$$

which itself forms a subtraction relationship,

$$5 \quad - \quad 3 \quad = \quad 2$$

This will work for all subtraction questions that do not require exchanges.

Follow-up ideas and questions

It would be interesting to explore the patterns formed by looking at the number of Egyptian numerals used when writing subtractions that involve exchanges.
e.g.

Q. Can you predict how many Egyptian numerals would be used to write down the result of any subtraction question?

Q. What patterns are formed if you look at the digital roots of subtractions written, using the numerals in our number system?

Egyptian Subtraction 1

Subtraction was the opposite process to addition and was often really simple because you just took away that number of numerals.

The symbol for subtraction was ⟁ .

	stood for	1
∩	stood for	10
ℰ	stood for	100
⚱	stood for	1000

For example: ∩∩∩∩∩|||| |||| ⟁ ∩∩∩|||| ⟺ ∩∩||||

      (58)   take away   (34)   equals   (24)

Do these subtractions using Egyptian Hieroglyphic numerals:
(you may want to check them by using our numerals and writing them underneath)

1 ∩∩∩∩∩|||| ||| ⟁ ∩∩||| ⟺

2 ℰ∩∩∩||||| ⟁ ∩∩|| ⟺

3 ℰℰ∩∩∩||| ∩∩ ⟁ ℰ∩∩∩| ⟺

4 ℰℰℰℰ∩∩|||||| ⟁ ℰℰ∩∩|| ⟺

5 ℰℰℰℰℰ∩∩∩||| ∩∩∩||| ⟁ ℰ∩∩||| ∩||| ⟺

6 ⚱ℰℰ∩∩∩||| ∩∩ ⟁ ℰℰ∩∩∩||| ∩∩ ⟺

7 ℰℰ∩∩∩∩∩∩|| ⚱∩∩ ⟁ ℰ∩∩|| ⚱ ⟺

8 ℰℰℰℰ⚱⚱⚱⚱ ℰℰℰ||| || ⟁ ℰℰ⚱⚱|||| ⟺

9 ℰℰ⚱⚱ ℰ∩∩|| ∩∩ ⟁ ℰℰ⚱⚱ ℰ∩∩|| ∩∩ ⟺

CHALLENGE

Count the number of Egyptian hieroglyphic numerals that are used in each number in the subtraction questions above. What kind of pattern can you spot? Make up some questions for a partner to do, that involve this kind of pattern.

Egyptian Subtraction 2

Subtraction was the opposite process to addition and sometimes involved having to exchange numerals.

∩   **ten** could be exchanged for **ten ones** ||||| |||||

𐦠   **hundred** could be exchanged for **ten tens**   ∩∩∩∩∩ ∩∩∩∩∩

𐦡   **thousand** could be exchanged for **ten hundred**   𐦠𐦠𐦠𐦠𐦠

For example:

∩∩∩∩ || ∧   ∩ |||| ⊟

(42)   take away   (13)   needs some exchanges

∩∩∩ ||||| || ∩ |||| would leave   ∩∩ |||||
|||||

because there are not enough **one** numerals to take away **three ones**.

Do these subtractions that need some exchanges:
(you may want to use the other side of this paper to work out the exchanges)

1 ∩∩∩||| ∧   ∩ ||||| ⊟

2 ∩∩∩∩   ∧ ||||| ⊟

3 ∩ ||||| ∧ |||||| ⊟
||| ||

4 𐦠∩∩   ∧ || ⊟

5 𐦠∩∩|| ∧   ∩ ||||| ⊟

6 𐦠∩∩∩∩||| ∧   ∩∩∩ ||||| ⊟

7 𐦠𐦠𐦠∩∩∩|||| ∧   ∩∩∩∩   ⊟
∩∩∩

8 𐦡𐦠𐦠𐦠𐦠𐦠∩∩   ∧   𐦠𐦠∩∩∩   ⊟

CHALLENGE

Set a partner some subtractions
involving exchanges.

Activity Sheets 7, 8 and 9   Pyramid Numbers

Task

In Activity Sheet 7, children are involved in adding up numbers in adjacent squares and placing the total in a square above. The challenge invites them to explore the number of ways it is possible to arrange 1, 2, 3 and 4 and arrive at different totals.

In Activity Sheet 8, they are also involved in colouring-in the odd numbers. The challenge invites children to make up some pyramid numbers for a partner and predict whether the total would be odd or even.

Activity Sheet 9 involves children in working out the missing numbers from partially completed pyramid grids. In the challenge they are invited to explore the different possible starting numbers needed to make a pyramid number of 30.

Mathematics

In Activity Sheet 7, children are adding together one- and two-digit numbers. The challenge will involve them in looking for all the possible ways of arranging four digits and the relationship between their position in the bottom row and the total at the top. This provides an opportunity for children to develop a logical and systematic way of working.

In Activity Sheet 8, the addition involves larger two-digit numbers and how odd and even totals are obtained by adding two numbers together. The challenge gives an opportunity to explore the relationship between odd and even numbers and make predictions about the result of adding them together.

In Activity Sheet 9, children are using and applying their knowledge of the relationship between addition and subtraction facts with an opportunity to use logical thought. The challenge involves an in-depth exploration of the range of possibilities with one total.

Possible outcomes

The different ways or arranging numbers 1, 2, 3 and 4 are interesting and require some system in order to be certain about finding them all.

One possibility is:

1234	2134	There are 6 ways starting with 1;
1243	2143	6 starting with 2; 6 starting with3;
1324	......	and 6 with 4.
1342	......	24 ways of arranging the numbers.
1423	......	
1432	......	

The number of different pyramid numbers obtained is, however, much smaller because some arrangements

yield the same total: 1 2 3 4 and 4 3 2 1 for instance.

The only totals possible are: 16, 18, 20, 22 and 24. The patterns of odd and even numbers in a pyramid grid are fascinating. Some of the conclusions children may express could include:

All even numbers in the bottom row will always give an even pyramid number.

All odd numbers in the bottom row will always give an even pyramid number.

If there are only two odd numbers in the bottom row but they are adjacent to one another then the pyramid number will always be even.

There are many other statements that could be made.

There are hundreds of possible groups of starting numbers that will give a pyramid number of 30. If fraction, decimal, and negative numbers are included, then the total rises still further. Children could work together to classify and sort their results.

Follow-up ideas and questions

There are three Resource Sheets: Pyramid Grids 3, 4, and 5, to support children's work. These contain empty pyramid grids for exploring pyramid numbers that use 3, 4 and 5 numbers in the bottom row. Children could be encouraged to find ways of working out what the pyramid number would be for any arrangement of three numbers in the bottom row of a pyramid grid.

e.g.

Q. What is the highest pyramid number possible using the numbers 2, 3 and 4?

Q. What would be the lowest?

Q. What is the highest and lowest pyramid number using 4, 7 and 9?

Children could be encouraged to explore pyramid numbers using four numbers in the bottom row in order to find the maximum and minimum pyramid number possible.

e.g.

Q. How many different pyramid numbers are possible using the numbers 2, 4, 5 and 7?

Q. Can a way of finding the pyramid number, with any arrangement of numbers in the bottom row, be found?

Q. What about using five numbers in the bottom row of a pyramid grid?

Q. How many possibilities are there, using numbers 1, 2, 3, 4 and 5?

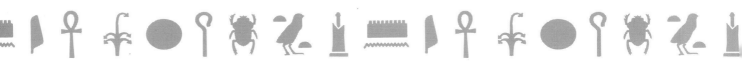

Pyramid Numbers 1

Pyramid numbers are made by putting a number
in each square in the bottom row of a pyramid grid.

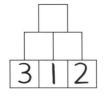

You then add the two numbers that are next to each other
and put the total in the square that is above them

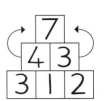

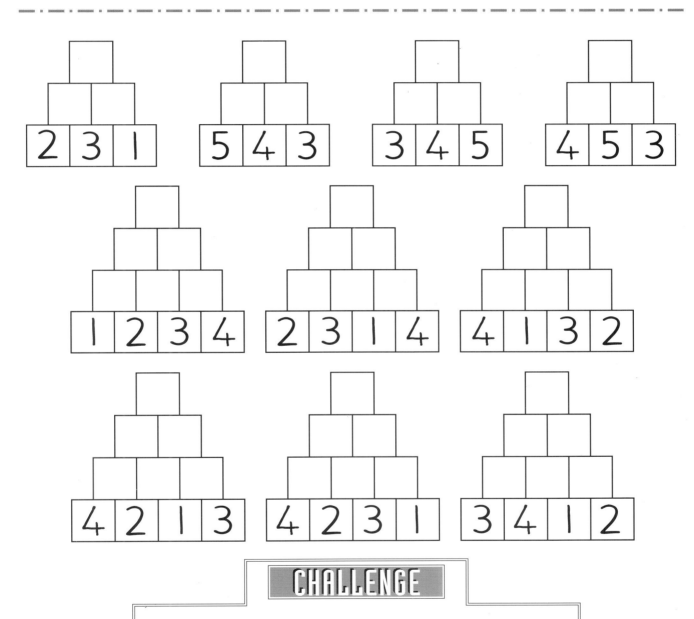

CHALLENGE

In how many different ways can you arrange
the numbers 1, 2, 3 and 4 in the bottom row of a
pyramid grid? How many different pyramid numbers do you get at the top?
Which numbers are impossible to get? Can you devise a way of working out
what the pyramid numbers will be?

Pyramid Numbers 2

Pyramid numbers are made by putting any number in each square in the bottom row, then adding the two numbers next to each other and putting the total in the square above.

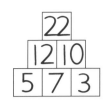

Work out these pyramid numbers.

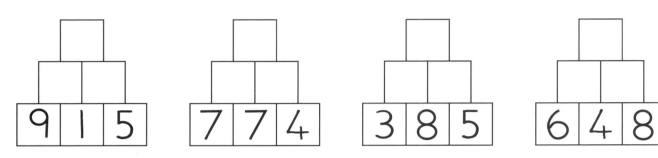

Work out these pyramid numbers but also colour in all the odd numbers?

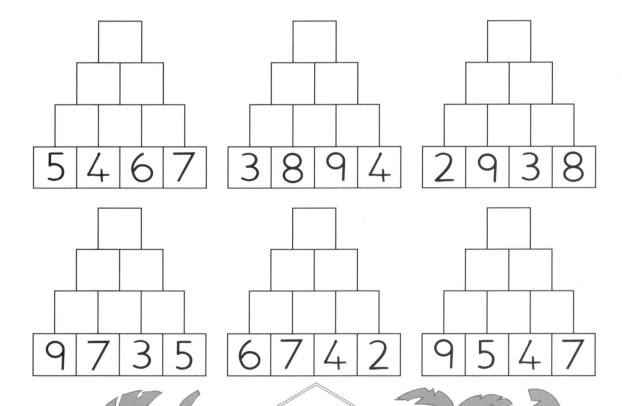

CHALLENGE

Make up some pyramid numbers for a partner to do. Challenge your partner to predict whether the pyramid number will be odd or even. What numbers would you have to put in the bottom row to make sure of getting an even pyramid number?

Pyramid Numbers 3

Pyramid numbers are made by putting any number in each square in the bottom row, then adding the two numbers next to each other and putting the total in the square above.

Work out the missing numbers in these pyramid grids.

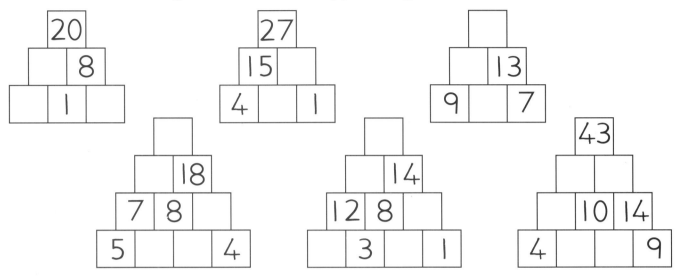

Work out what the numbers are in the bottom row.

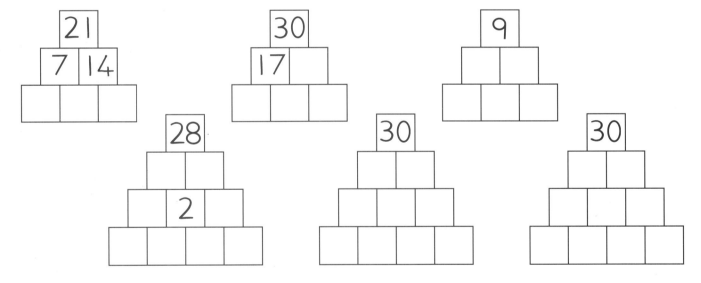

CHALLENGE

If a pyramid number
is 30, how many arrangements of
numbers would be possible in the bottom row
of a pyramid grid? What possible three numbers could
you start with? What possible four numbers could you start with?

Activity Sheets 10 and 11   Egyptian Multiplication

Task

In Activity Sheet 10, children will be doubling numbers to find 2, 4 and 8 times a number. The challenge involves them in setting questions for a partner.

Activity Sheet 11 involves using a doubling and adding method to carry out other multiplications. The challenge sets some additional questions involving larger numbers and invites children to work out some questions of their own to check with a calculator or by using another method.

Mathematics

In Activity Sheet 10, children will be using a mental method to double numbers. They will be using and applying their knowledge of place value and the relationships between multiples of 2, 4 and 8. The challenge involves them in additionally recognising the relationships between multiples of 8, 16 and 32.

In Activity Sheet 11, children will be examining the relationship between multiplication and addition being developed using additions of multiples of 2, 4 and 8, extending to 16, in the challenge.

Possible outcomes

Children don't often realise the interconnections between numbers in the multiplication tables and learning them is sometimes made easier if they can be helped to see the relationships more clearly. Some children may see that:

$4 \times$ any number $= 2 \times 2$ that number

and

$8 \times$ any number $= 2 \times 2 \times 2$ that number

and

$16 \times$ any number $= 2 \times 2 \times 2 \times 2$ that number

and so on.

Some children may be able to express the relationships between addition and multiplication in a variety of ways. For instance:

$7 \times 14 =$

$(1 + 2 + 4) \times 14 =$

$(1 \times 14) + (2 \times 14) + (4 \times 14)$

$9 \times$ any number $=$

$(1 \times$ that number$) + (8 \times$ that number$) =$

$(1 + 8) \times$ number

Follow-up ideas

The patterns and relationships between multiples of numbers are both fascinating and numerous. Children could be encouraged to find other groups of multiples that are a result of doubling: 3, 6, 12 ... and 5, 10, 20 ...

Patterns in multiples can be easily seen if you look at them in an ordered arrangement of numbers like a hundred square.

e.g.

Q. What patterns and relationships can you see if you colour-in all multiples of 3 and 6?

Q. What about multiples of 2, 4 and 8? or 5 and 10?

Children could be encouraged to devise their own alternative method for carrying out multiplication. This would give them a wonderful opportunity to demonstrate what they know and understand about numbers, place value and the process of multiplication.

The multiplication methods used by people from other countries and cultures could also be explored.

e.g.

Q. What is Russian Multiplication?

Q. Which methods of multiplication do you find easiest to perform and why?

Egyptian Multiplication 1

The Egyptians did not need to know their times tables to do multiplication because all they used was the two times table, or doubling a number.

Double these numbers:

1 Double 24 is _____   **2** Double 35 is _____

3 Double 19 is _____   **4** Double 29 is _____

5 Double 72 is _____   **6** Double 108 is _____

To find out what four times any number was they doubled two times the number. Example:

4×13 Double 13 is 26,   double it, is 52.

(2×13) (4×13)

Double, double each of these numbers:

7 4×23 Double 23 is _____   double it is _____

8 4×17 Double 17 is _____   double it is _____

9 4×45 Double 45 is _____   double it is _____

10 4×61 Double 61 is _____   double it is _____

To find out what eight times any number was, the Egyptians doubled four times that number. For example:

8×24 would be: 24   is 1×24

double it   48   is 2×24

double it   96   is 4×24

double it   192   is 8×24

Work out eight times this number:

11 8×31 would be: 31   is 1×31

double it   _____   is 2×31

double it   _____   is 4×31

double it   _____   is 8×31

CHALLENGE

Set some questions for a partner to do that involve multiplying by 4 and 8. Try some that are multiplications by 16 and 32 using the doubling method.

Egyptian Multiplication 2

The Egyptians used a doubling and adding method to do their multiplications.

For example: 9×15

15	was	1×15
~~30~~	was	~~2×15~~
~~60~~	was	~~4×15~~
120	was	8×15
135	was	9×15

They knew that 9×15
was the same as $(1+8) \times 15$
so they added those amounts together and crossed off the rest.

(you might want to check this answer your own way)

Try these multiplications using the Egyptian method:

1 7×14

_____ is 1×14

_____ is 2×14

_____ is 4×14

_____ is 7×14

2 9×21

_____ is 1×21

_____ is 2×21

_____ is 4×21

_____ is 8×21

_____ is 9×21

3 12×45

_____ is 1×45

_____ is 2×45

_____ is 4×45

_____ is 8×45

_____ is 12×45

4 13×17

_____ is 1×17

_____ is 2×17

_____ is 4×17

_____ is 8×17

_____ is 13×17

Use the other side of this paper to work out these multiplication questions

5 7×103

6 9×215

7 12×43

8 13×65

CHALLENGE

Work out these multiplications using the Egyptian method:

9 13×27

10 17×45

11 19×53

12 23×126

Work out some multiplications of your own and then check them using a calculator or another method.

Activity Sheet 12   Pyramid Builders

Task

Children are asked to work out the distances that a ramp would need to be from a pyramid of a given height and the height of pyramids when the ramp distance is given, when the slope is 1 in 12. The challenge involves them in working out what the slope would be for a variety of different pyramid and ramp measurements and work out which would be the steepest.

Mathematics

Children will be involved in recognising the need for multiplication by 12 and carrying out calculations with multiples of 10. Some questions will involve them in recognising the need for dividing by twelve and working this out using multiples of 10. They will need to interpret the question and use logical thought. The challenge involves children in recognising simple factors of numbers in multiples of 30 and realising that this can be represented as a slope where the steepest slope is 1 in 'smallest number'.

Possible outcomes

The challenge invites children to draw or imagine what the slopes of 1 in 1, 1 in 2, 1 in 4 and 1 in 3.5 would look like. These can be represented by an interesting set of right-angled triangles where the angle, made by the slope from the horizontal line, gets bigger as the 'number' gets smaller.

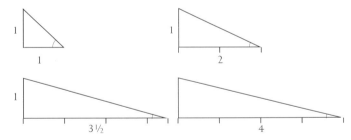

Children may come up with a variety of statements describing how the angle gets smaller as the length of the base line gets longer.

Follow-up ideas and questions

The Resource Sheet: The Great Pyramid gives facts and measurements about this pyramid. Children could be encouraged to pose questions that are left unanswered in the text. These could be derived from information contained in the sheet.

e.g.

Q. What is the area of the square base of the Great Pyramid?

Q. Approximately how much would it weigh?

Q. How far away would the ramp need to be from the pyramid in order to drag up the last stone needed to build it?

Children could be invited to draw comparisons with the Great Pyramid and other great buildings. These could be represented in a variety of ways including scale drawings and models and graphs showing relevant data.

Children could be encouraged to explore other right-angled triangles and see what happens to the angle of slope, as the height and length are varied.

e.g.

Q. What happens to the angle when the length is increased by one unit each time?

Q. What happens when the height is increased by one unit each time?

Sets of triangles where the ratio description of the slope remains the same could be drawn. For instance, a ratio of 1 in 5 would give a set of triangle which includes those with the following lengths and heights:

length	height
5	1
10	2
15	3
...	...

Children could be encouraged to appreciate that the slope angle of each triangle would be the same. Explore the angle of a set of triangles with slope ratios of 1 in 2, or 1 in 4.

Q. What angle is made by these slopes?

Children could make a series of drawings or a scale model of a pyramid with the ramp shown, also to scale, to show the stages in which it might have been built. This would enable them to appreciate how the Egyptian engineers calculated where to build the pyramid so that the ramp in the final stage would be closest to the river.

Q. How far away from your school would a ramp need to be if your school was built in the same way as the Egyptians built their pyramids?

Pyramid Builders

It is thought that the Egyptians built ramps on which they dragged the stones needed to build the pyramids.

10 m

120 m

The slope needed to be kept at the same angle, so as the pyramid grew higher, the slope got longer.

20 m

240 m

100 m

The slopes were probably about 1 in 12.
This means that for every height of one unit of the pyramid, the ramp needed to be twelve units away.

With a slope of 1 in 12 work out these distances:

1 Pyramid 20 m high,   ramp _____ m away.

2 Pyramid 30 m high,   ramp _____ m away.

3 Pyramid 40 m high,   ramp _____ m away.

4 Pyramid _____ m high, ramp 600 m away.

5 Pyramid _____ m high, ramp 720 m away.

Still with a slope of 1 in 12 work out distances; they have not been arranged in any order.

6 Ramp is 960 m away,   pyramid _____ m high.

7 Ramp is 1200 m away, pyramid _____ m high.

8 Pyramid _____ m high, ramp 840 m away.

9 Pyramid _____ m high, ramp 2400 m away.

10 Ramp is _____ m away, pyramid is 90 m high.

CHALLENGE

Try to work out what the slope would be in these pyramid measurements.

Pyramid 30 m high, ramp 60 m away.

Slope is 1 in _____.

Pyramid 30 m high, ramp 30 m away.

Slope is 1 in _____.

Pyramid 30 m high, ramp 120 m away.

Slope is 1 in _____.

Pyramid 30 m high, ramp 105 m away.

Slope is 1 in _____.

Try imagining or drawing these slopes to find out which one would be the steepest. Make up some slopes for a partner to draw. What can you say about what you have found out?

Activity Sheet 13   Making Pyramids 1

Task

Children are asked to cut up the net of a square-based pyramid to make a pyramid and to make predictions about its height and the location of the apex. They are invited to look at the Resource Sheet: Making More Pyramids, for further ideas and suggestions.

Mathematics

Children are involved in using a 2D net to construct a 3D structure. They will be making predictions about how high the pyramid will be and where the apex will be in relation to the square base. This will involve them in estimation and interpretation of the meaning of the measurements in the net.

Possible outcomes

The top of the pyramid should be directly above the centre of the square base of the pyramid. Some children may be able to deduce that the height of the pyramid will be less than the height of the triangles on each side of the square. After making their pyramid children could be encouraged to look at their pyramids, measure the height and come to the realisation that because the triangle side is at an angle, this has the effect of reducing its height from the base of the pyramid.

Follow-up ideas and questions

Children could be encouraged to make other pyramids and the Resource Sheet: Making More Pyramids, contains a set of instructions for making a square-based pyramid of any size.

Q. Can you draw the net of a pyramid that has a base of 10 cms and an approximate height of 10 cms?

The Resource Sheet: Making More Pyramids, poses questions to encourage children to explore different possible heights of pyramids with the same sized square base.

Q. What can you say about the angle of the slope of pyramids that have the same sized base but different heights?

Children can be encouraged to make nets of pyramids with triangular bases. These can be right angled, isosceles or equilateral triangles and yield a wealth of opportunity for exploring the properties of triangles and pyramid structures, as well as giving experience of measuring for a purpose.

Q. Can you make a pyramid with a right-angle triangle base where the top of the pyramid is directly over the right angle corner of the base?

Q. Can you make a triangle with an equilateral triangle base where the top is directly over the centre of the base?

Making Pyramids 1

The Egyptians were expert pyramid builders and always made pyramids so that the top was exactly over the middle of the square base. You can make your own pyramids by using a flat plan called a net. This can be cut up and folded along the lines and glued together using the flaps.

Cut out and make a pyramid using the flat net below.

Try to predict how high you think the top will be above the base.

Do you think the top will be exactly over the middle of the square base? How do you know?

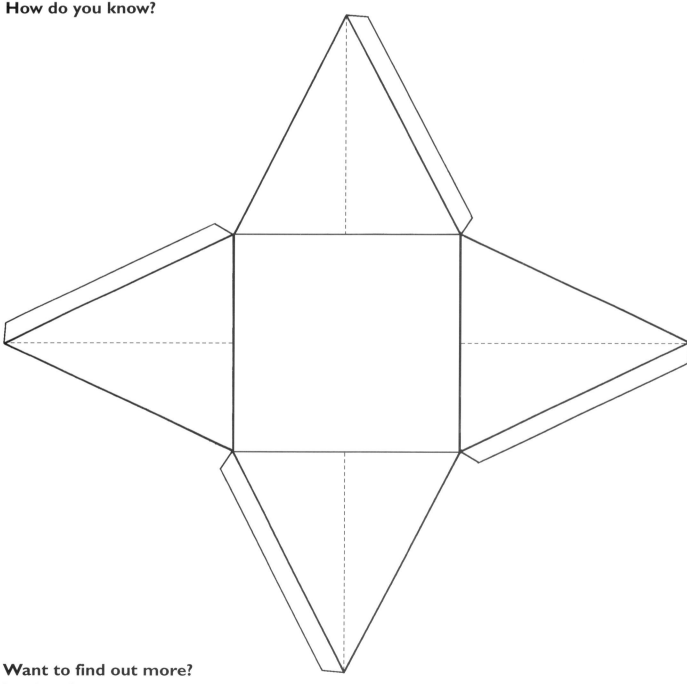

Want to find out more?
Look at ideas on the Resource Sheet: Making More Pyramids

Activity Sheet 14   Making Pyramids 2

Task

Children are invited to consider the total number of blocks needed to make pyramid structures of different heights. The challenge asks them to make a prediction for the number needed for a higher pyramid and to check their prediction using a variety of strategies.

Mathematics

Children will be involved in counting and recognising multiplication square numbers. They will also be engaged in adding together square numbers to find a total and putting numerical data into a table of results. The challenge involves them in making and verifying predictions about how the sequence of numbers continues. This will require using and applying appropriate strategies for solving the problem of how many blocks would be needed for a pyramid 10 and 20 blocks high.

Possible outcomes

Children will be adding up numbers in the following sequence:

$$1, \quad 4, \quad 9, \quad 16, \quad 25, \quad 36, \dots \quad n \times n \quad n^2$$

It would be interesting to note how they are performing these additions and see if they are using number bonds to 10, 20, 30 … as a helpful strategy on self-checking method.

There are interesting number patterns in the square numbers and some children may be using this observation as a strategy for continuing the sequence of numbers:

$$1, \quad 4, \quad 9, \quad 16, \quad 25, \quad 36, \dots$$
$$+3 \quad +5 \quad +7 \quad +9 \quad +11 \quad +13 \dots$$

Follow-up ideas and questions

There are many opportunities for developing algebra through the exploration of number patterns that can be generated by growing pyramid structures using bricks and cubes. Multilink and wooden cubes and lego can all be used to make pyramids from which counting the pieces used in successive pyramids will generate an interesting number pattern.

Use multilink cubes to generate pyramids and invite children to predict how many will be needed to make the next pyramid in a sequence.

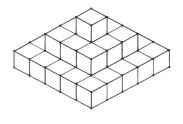

This may involve children in looking at the following number pattern:

height of pyramid	cubes in each layer	total cubes
1	1	1
2	1 + 9	10
3	1 + 9 + 25	35

Q. How many cubes would be needed to make a pyramid 10 cubes high?

Q. If there are 81 cubes in the bottom layer, how high would the pyramid be?

Q. How many cubes would there be in the bottom layer of a pyramid 100 cubes high?

Children could be encouraged to give reasons and justifications for their answers?

Using lego bricks to generate pyramids invites all sorts of additional possibilities. There are different types of bricks and different patterns will be generated by each type. It is often more helpful to be consistent in the type of brick used to make each group of pyramids as this is more likely to yield a predictable pattern in the number of bricks.

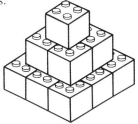

As well as counting the number of bricks you can count the number of raised dots on each layer or step of the pyramid. This may involve children in looking at the following number pattern:

height of pyramid	raised dots seen in each layer	analysis
1	4	(1×4)
2	4 + 12	$(1 \times 4) + (3 \times 4)$
3	4 + 12 + 20	$(1 \times 4) + (3 \times 4) + (5 \times 4)$
4	4 + 12 + 20 + 28	…

It is usually helpful to analyse what is happening as each layer of data grows as the patterns are more obvious. Encouraging children to look at how the data relates to the diagrams of structures made also helps to identify and make sense of the information.

Q. Why is the number of dots in each layer increasing in multiples of 4?

Q. How many dots would you see in each layer of a pyramid 8 cubes high?

Q. If I am standing on 44 dots in a pyramid layer, how many steps would take me to the top?

Making Pyramids 2

The Egyptians made their pyramids by cutting stone blocks and placing them in layers in a square arrangement, one layer on top of another, getting smaller and smaller as they got to the top. They would need to predict how many blocks they would use to make pyramids of different sizes.

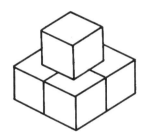

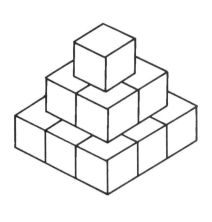

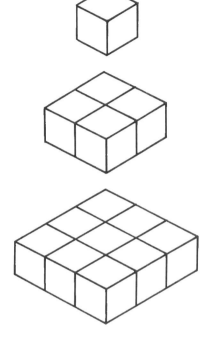

Questions

You may find it helpful to use cubes to make these pyramids.

1 In the pyramid 3 blocks high how many blocks are needed all together? _____

2 How many blocks would be needed to make a pyramid that was 4 blocks high? _____

3 How many would be needed to make the pyramid 5 blocks high? _____

4 Put your results in some kind of order and fill in the table below. _____

Height of Pyramid	1 block	2 blocks	3 blocks	4 blocks	5 blocks
Total number of blocks needed					

CHALLENGE
Predict how many blocks would be needed to make a pyramid 10 blocks high. Check your prediction by drawing a diagram or making the pyramid or continuing with the table of results above. What about 20 blocks high?

Activity Sheet 15 Pharaohs

Task

Children are given pictures and information about nine Pharaohs. This includes the years of their rule, the age when they came to power and when they died. Some of the information is missing however, and they are invited to work out what it is. They are then asked to cut out the Pharaohs and put them in order, from who reigned first.

Mathematics

Children will be involved in working out differences in years, between two dates and using information involving dates to calculate how long someone lived or the age they were when they died. They will be using and applying logical thought and their knowledge of place value up to thousands, to make calculations and arrange dates in chronological order.

Possible outcomes

Further information about Pharaohs lives can be obtained from the Resource Sheet: Pharaohs, which lists all the Dynasties and identifies who reigned during them, and for how long. This provides both a check-list and a source for follow-up work using time lines.

Follow-up ideas and questions

Some children may be helped by being able to use a number line or date line where dates are arranged in order in intervals of 1000 or 100 years. This would provide a way of grouping dates according to which century they were in and ordering in decades is then made more accessible. Children could work in groups and be encouraged to find out interesting events that happened during a particular century and display their findings presented in chronological order.

The Information Sheet: Time Line, provides a time line, listing the main periods of Egyptian civilisation with brief details about each. This could provide a structure for ordering the dates of events by enabling them to be placed within a particular period of time.

All dates have been matched with those in the *British Museum Book of Ancient Egypt*. Edited by Stephen Quirke and Jeffrey Spencer, published by the British Museum Press 1992.

Egyptian Pharaohs

Fill in the missing information about these Pharaohs. Cut them out then arrange them in order from who reigned first to who reigned last.

Khufu

Khufu built the great pyramid. He reigned from 2551 BC to 2528 BC. He reigned for _____ years.

Rameses II

Rameses reigned for 66 years. He came to the throne in 1279 BC. He died in _____ BC.

Amenhotep III

Amenhotep came to the throne in 1390 BC. He reigned for 38 years. He died in _____ BC.

Tutankhamun

Tutankhamun was king when he was eight years old. He ruled from 1336 to 1327 BC. When he died he was _____ years old.

Hatshepsut

Hatshepsut ruled with her son Thutmose III from 1479 BC to 1425 BC. She ruled for _____ years.

Djoser

Djoser had the first step pyramid built. He ruled for 19 years. He died in 2611 BC. He came to the throne in _____ BC.

Cleopatra

Cleopatra killed herself in 30 BC. She came to the throne in 51 BC. She ruled for _____ years.

Senusret III

Senusret conquered the land of Nubia and ruled from 1874 to 1855 BC. He was pharaoh for _____ years.

Chephren

Chephren died in 2494 BC He was pharaoh for 26 years. He came to the throne in _____ BC.

Resource Sheets: Outline of Content

These sheets support many of the activities suggested earlier and could be used in a variety of ways. They are not 'stand alone' pages but 'content free' and would require some introduction by the teacher to provide a focus for the work of children.

Number	Title	Outline of content
1	**Egyptian Numerals**	Hieroglyphic, Hieratic and Demotic scripts.
2	**Pyramid Grid 3**	Empty pyramid grid using 3 numbers in base.
3	**Pyramid Grid 4**	Empty pyramid grid using 4 numbers in base.
4	**Pyramid Grid 5**	Empty pyramid grid using 5 numbers in base.
5	**The Great Pyramid**	Measurements and information about the Great Pyramid.
6	**Making More Pyramids**	Instructions: how to make pyramids of any size.
7	**Weights and Measures**	List of measures used by Ancient Egyptians.
8	**The Game of Seega**	Outline of board and rules for the game.
9	**Nine Men's Morris**	Outline of board and rules for the game.

Information Sheets: Outline of Content

These two sheets support some of the activities suggested earlier and could be used by the teacher in a variety of ways. They provide factual information that could be used in conjunction with the children's mathematical work on or within a general topic of Ancient Egypt.

Number	Title	Outline of content
1	**Map of Ancient Egypt**	Map showing the extent of Ancient Egypt.
2	**Time Line**	Time line showing main periods and dynasties.

Egyptian Numerals

Hieroglyphic	
unit	I
ten	∩
hundred	ℓ
thousand	⚘
tens of thousands	𓆐
hundreds of thousands	𓁨

Hieratic

	1	2	3	4	5	6	7	8	9
units	I	II	III	—	⅃	!!!	ʓ	=	ⱴ
tens	⋏	⋏̄	˙⋏	⁚	ꜱ	⊔⊔	⋎	⊔⊔⊔	⊔⊔⊔
hundreds	ﾉ	ﾉﾞ	ﾞﾞﾂ	˙˙ﾂ	˙˙ﾂ	ﾞﾂ	⅄ﾞ	˙ﾞﾂ	ﾞﾂ
thousands	⅙	ﾞﾞﾋ	ﾞﾞﾋ	ﾞﾋ	ﾞﾋﾋ	ﾋ	ﾋ	⎕	⎕

Demotic

	1	2	3	4	5	6	7	8	9
units	I	⅄	♭	⌄	⁊	⅄	—	ⅎ	⁊
tens	⋏	ꝭ	⅄	∠	ⅎ	⅄	⅄	ⅎ	ⱪ
hundreds	ﾉ	ﾉ	⅄	⅄	ⅎ	⅄	ⅎ	⅄	ⅎ
thousands	⅄	ⅎ	ⅎ	ⅎ	ⅎ	ⅎ	ⅎ	ⅎ	ⅎ

Pyramid Grids 3

Pyramid Grids 4

© 1994 The Educational Television Company Ltd.

Pyramid Grids 5

The Great Pyramid

The Great Pyramid was the largest pyramid built by the Egyptians and was built at Giza for King Khufu in 2528 BC. It took 20 years to build.

Pyramids had to be built on the west side of the Nile because this was the side on which the sun set. They had to be on ground high enough to protect them from the flood waters and on a rock base that would be stone enough to carry the weight of the pyramid.

   The Great Pyramid was built using 2.3 million limestone blocks.
   Blocks ranged from 2.5 to 15 tonnes in weight.

Pyramids had to be near enough to the river so that the stones needed to build it did not have to be carried too far. The stones were thought to be dragged up a ramp that had a slope of 1 in 12. That meant for every metre in height of a pyramid, the ramp needed to be 12 meters away.

   The Great Pyramid was 146 metres in height.
   This is taller than the Statue of Liberty (92 metres) and St. Pauls Cathedral (110 metres).

Pyramids were always built on a square base. This square had to be positioned in a special way. Each side had to face one of the cardinal points. These were north, south, east and west. It is thought that the Egyptians used the positions of the stars to determine north.

The square base of a pyramid was made level by clearing away sand to show the bare rock, then making rows of channels which were flooded by the river.

Clearing the sand to expose the bare rock

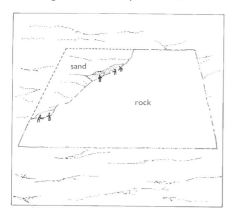

Levelling the site
a. marking out the correct level

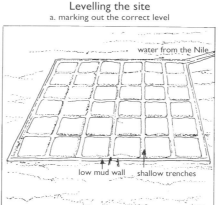

Levelling the site
b. cutting away the surplus stone and filling in the holes

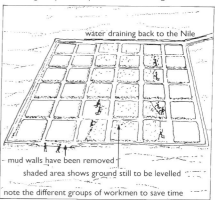

The Great Pyramid has one corner only about one centimetre higher than all the others which is an amazing achievement, considering the area covered by the base of the pyramid.

   The Great Pyramid has a square base of 245 metres in length.
   This is almost the same area as seven and a half football pitches.

Near the Great Pyramid, lodgings or barracks for 4,000 men have been found.

Making More Pyramids

You will need:

▲ a pencil   ▲ a ruler   ▲ paper with cm squares on it   ▲ a pair of scissors

Instructions

1 Draw a square, in the middle of the cm squared paper, that is the size of your pyramid's base.

2 Make a mark half-way along each side of the square.

3 Draw a faint line, at right-angles to each side of your square the approximate height you want your pyramid to be.

4 Draw triangles on each side of your square so that the faint line is halving the triangle.

5 Mark in flaps along one side of each triangle.

6 Cut out, fold along lines and glue flaps to make your pyramid.

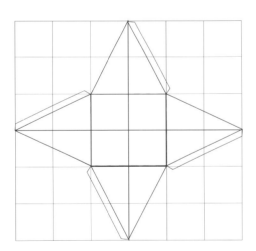
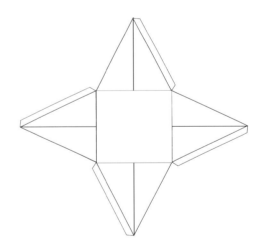

You will need to decide:

▲ the size of the square base – how long each side of the square will be

▲ the approximate height of your pyramid – the height of the triangle drawn on each side of the square

Explore:

Making pyramids that have the same size square base but different heights. What can you find out about the angle of the sloping side of these pyramids?

Weights and Measures

Measurements of length

Ancient Egyptians measured short lengths using parts of a man's arm and hand. They based their measurements on the Royal Cubit. This was about the length of the forearm and was approximately 52.5 cm. The smallest unit was a finger, called a digit. Four digits equalled one palm, and seven palms equalled one cubit.

    4 digits = 1 palm (approx. 7.5 cm)
    7 palms = 1 cubit (approx. 52.5 cm)

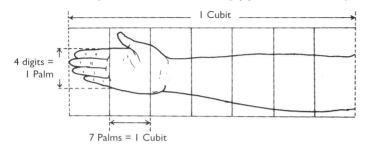

Longer distances were called the rod and atons.

    100 cubits = 1 rod (called a khet)
    20,000 cubits = 1 aton

Measures of area

A rectangle area which was one cubit wide and 100 cubits long was also called a cubit. The Egyptians ignored any word corresponding to square. Using our measures, this cubit was equal to 27.35 square metres.

    100 cubits = 1 khet (this was a square area)

If they wanted smaller areas, the Egyptians divided the khet into $\frac{1}{8}$, $\frac{1}{4}$ and $\frac{1}{2}$. ($\frac{1}{2}$ of a square khet was a rmn)

Measures of capacity

The hekat was the official measure of amounts of corn. Smaller measures were in fractions of the hekat,$= \frac{1}{2}, \frac{1}{4}, \frac{1}{8}, \frac{1}{16}, \frac{1}{32}$, and $\frac{1}{64}$. These were written in the symbol known as the Horus Eye. There is a legend that the God Horus had an eye torn apart in a fight and the parts were later restored by the God Thoth.

32 ro = 1 hin
10 of these hin (called hennu) = 1 hekat
20 or 16 hekat = 1 khar (or sack)

The hekat was approximately 4.89 litres

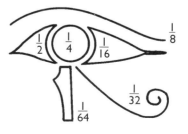

The measurement of weight

Egyptians used the kite and the deben as their measures for the weight of metals. The deben weighed approximately 14 grams. It was later revalued at 91 grams.

    1 deben = 10 kite

Seega

Seega is a up to date version of an old game.
It still is a very popular game in Egypt.

Rules

▲ It is a game for two players.

▲ Each has three counters of their own colour.

▲ The game starts with the pieces in this position.

▲ Players can move 1 or 2 squares in a straight
line – horizontally, vertically, or diagonally.

▲ They cannot pass over another piece.

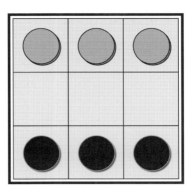

The winner makes a straight line of three counters (horizontally, vertically, or diagonally).
The straight line may not be a player's original line.

Nine Men's Morris

This game and a variety of different version has been played in many countries for hundreds of years. Boards dating back to 1400 BC have been found in Egypt.

Rules

▲ It is a game for two players. Each has nine counters of their own colour.
▲ The game starts with no pieces on the board. Players place pieces alternately until all are on the board.
▲ Players take turns to move pieces along lines to a neighbouring empty point.
▲ When a player has three in a row (a mill), an opposing counter is removed but it must not be taken from an opposing mill.

If a player is reduced to two pieces or is blocked and unable to move, they have lost the game.

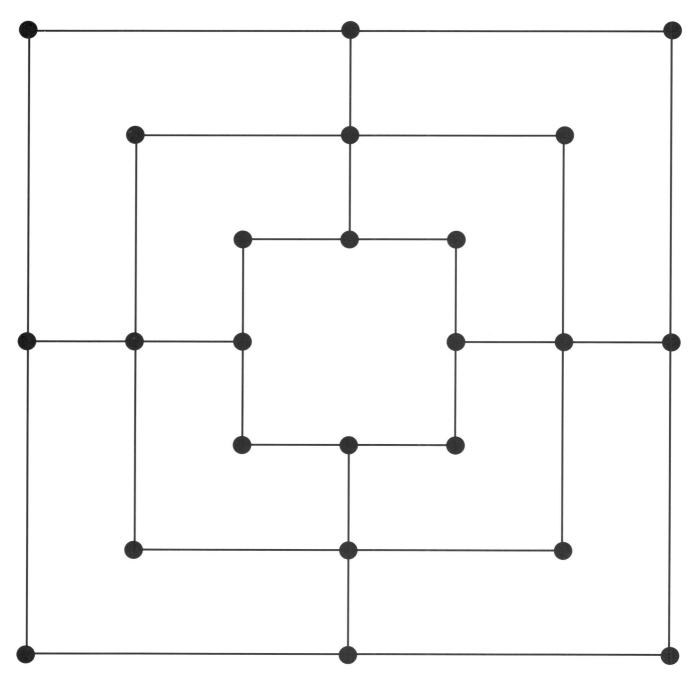

Map of Ancient Egypt

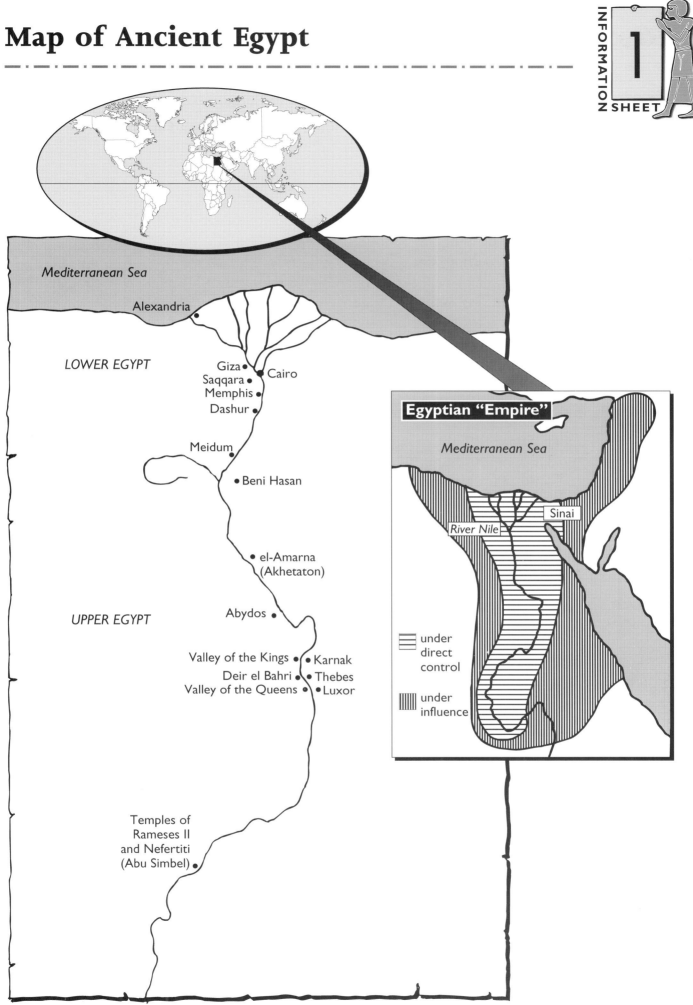

Mediterranean Sea

Alexandria

LOWER EGYPT

Giza
Saqqara
Memphis
Cairo
Dashur

Meidum

Beni Hasan

el-Amarna
(Akhetaton)

UPPER EGYPT

Abydos

Valley of the Kings
Deir el Bahri
Valley of the Queens
Karnak
Thebes
Luxor

Temples of
Rameses II
and Nefertiti
(Abu Simbel)

Egyptian "Empire"

Mediterranean Sea

River Nile

Sinai

under
direct
control

under
influence

Dates and Dynasties

Period	Year	Dynasty
The Early Dynastic Period (c 3100–2613 BC)	4000 BC	Earliest settlements on banks of the Nile.
	3500 BC	Separate Upper and Lower Kingdoms.
	3100 BC	**Dynasties 1–3** Beginning of united kingdom of Upper and Lower Egypt under the Pharoahs.
	3000 BC	First centralised government, Princes of This.
	2630 BC	Step pyramid built.
The Old Kingdom (c 2613–2160 BC)	2613 BC	**Dynasties 4–8** Pyramid Age and pioneering period. Great Pyramid built.
The First Intermediate Period (c 2160–2060 BC)	2160 BC	**Dynasties 9–11** Time of social revolution, weakened power of the royals.
The Middle Kingdom (c 2040–1750 BC)	2040 BC	**Dynasties 11–13** Time of great literary activity. Senusret III launched campaigns in Nubi.
The Second Intermediate Period (c 1750–1650 BC)	1750 BC	**Dynasties 13–17** Egypt subjugated by Asiatic invaders.
The New Kingdom (c 1550–1086 BC)	1550 BC	**Dynasties 18–20** Greatest imperial expansion.
	1336 BC	Tutankhamun was king.
	1153 BC	Rameses III was assassinated.
The Third Intermediate Period (c 1086–661 BC)	1086 BC	**Dynasties 21–25** Period of national decline. Assyrian and Persian invaders.
The Late Period (661–332 BC)	661 BC	**Dynasties 26–30**
	359 BC	Last native Egyptian Pharoah, Nectanebo. Wars and invasion from Persia.
The Ptolemaic Period (332–30 BC)	332 BC	Ruled by Greek monarchs, after conquest by Alexander the Great. The last monarch was Cleopatra.
Roman Period (30–AD 642)	30 BC	Egypt incorporated into the Roman Empire.
Islamic conquest of Egypt	642 AD	